Produced by
Alfred Music Publishing Co., Inc.
P.O. Box 10003
Van Nuys, CA 91410-0003
alfred.com

Arranged by Bill Galliford, Ethan Neuburg and Tod Edmondson

ISBN-10: 0-7390-4997-6
ISBN-13: 978-0-7390-4997-6

Contents

Harry Potter
AND THE
SORCERER'S
STONE

GODRIC GRYFFINDOR
Harry Potter
AND THE
CHAMBER
OF SECRETS

DOUBLE TROUBLE

Music by
JOHN WILLIAMS

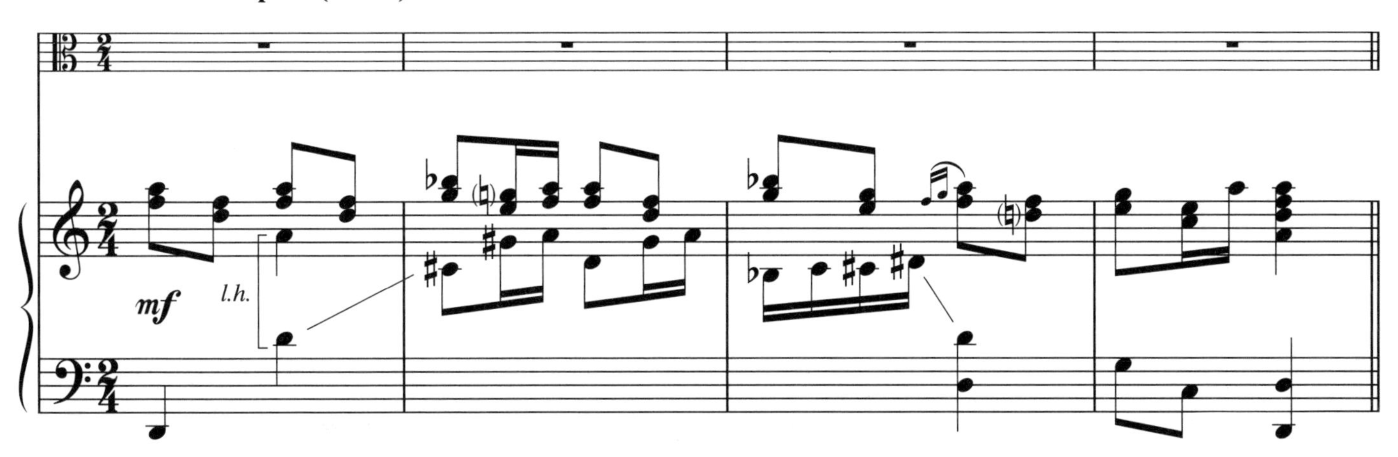

15

sim.

l.h.

28
sim.

38
sim.
48
Driving now, with a "swagger"

FAWKES THE PHOENIX

Music by
JOHN WILLIAMS

14
f
f
26
mf
mf

*An easier 8th-note alternative figure has been provided.

42
f
f
mp
mp
p
pp

FIREWORKS

By NICHOLAS HOOPER

11
19

27

cresc.
35
f
decresc.
3
mf
mp
mf

47
mf
55

61
f
cresc.
f
cresc.
ff
ff

HEDWIG'S THEME

By **JOHN WILLIAMS**

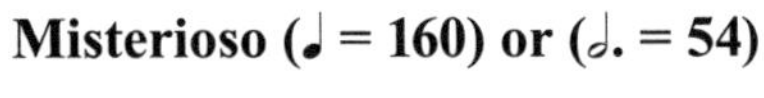

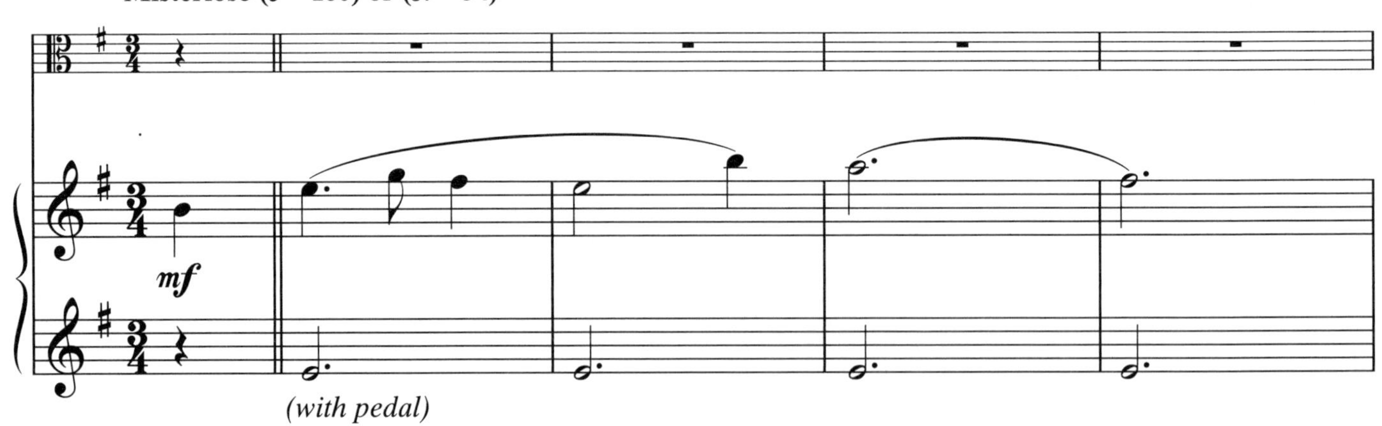

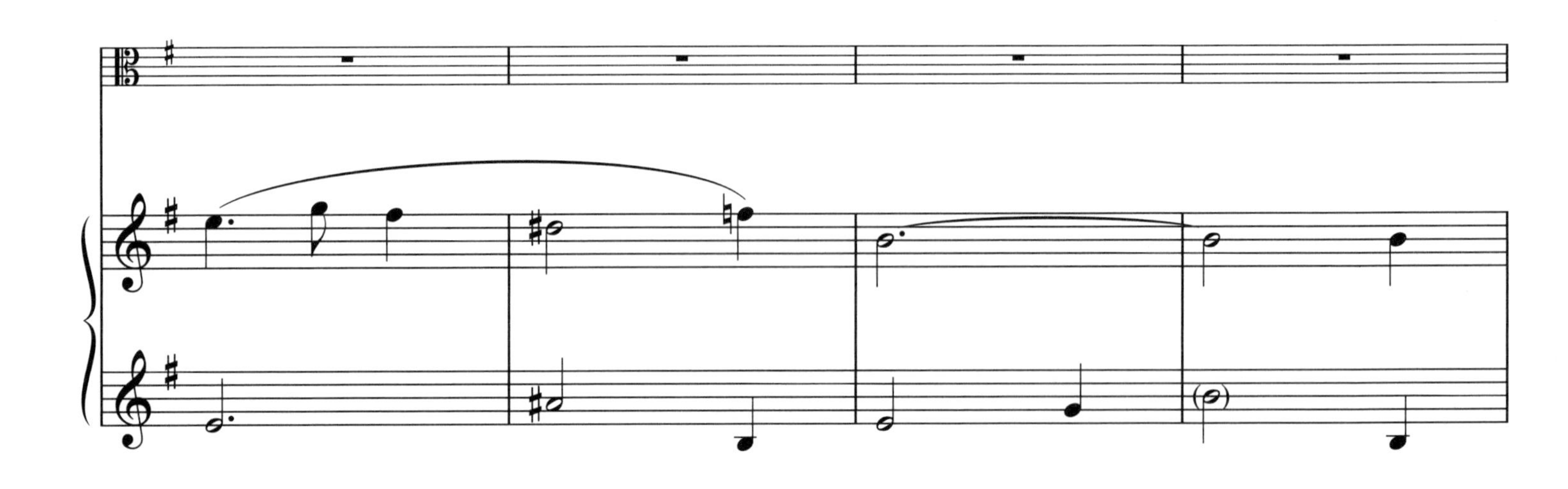

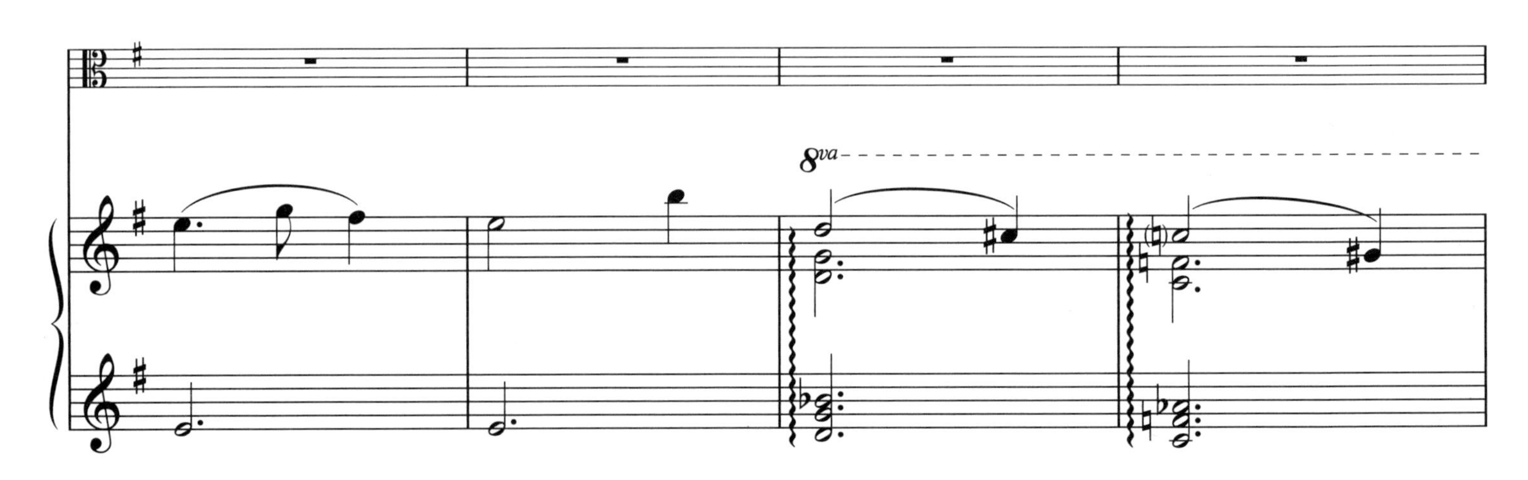

(8va)
mf
17

* A♯ = B♭.

51
Bright (𝅗𝅥 = 80)
mf

59
mf
p
p

HARRY'S WONDROUS WORLD

Music by
JOHN WILLIAMS

mf
26
f
f
mf
mf

mp
mf
42
mf
mp
mp

50
mf
mf
3
3
3
3
2
1
2
2
58
f
f

Viola

Level 2–3

Selections from Harry Potter

Instrumental Solos (Movies 1–5)

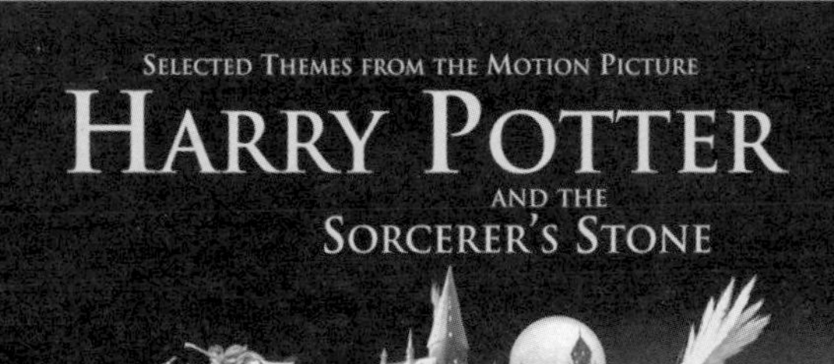

Level 2–3

Contents

Produced by
Alfred Music Publishing Co., Inc.
P.O. Box 10003
Van Nuys, CA 91410-0003
alfred.com

Arranged by Bill Galliford, Ethan Neuburg and Tod Edmondson

ISBN-10: 0-7390-4997-6
ISBN-13: 978-0-7390-4997-6

DOUBLE TROUBLE

Music by
JOHN WILLIAMS

FAWKES THE PHOENIX

Music by
JOHN WILLIAMS

*An easier 8th-note alternative figure has been provided.

FIREWORKS

By NICHOLAS HOOPER

35
12
47
mf
4
55
61
f
ff

HEDWIG'S THEME

By **JOHN WILLIAMS**

*A♯ = B♭.

HARRY'S WONDROUS WORLD

Music by
JOHN WILLIAMS

50
mf
58
f
66
2
82 Victoriously
f
90 Broadly
4

*The top cue notes are provided as a performing alternative.

PROFESSOR UMBRIDGE

By NICHOLAS HOOPER

2
42
(V)
57

NIMBUS 2000

Music by
JOHN WILLIAMS

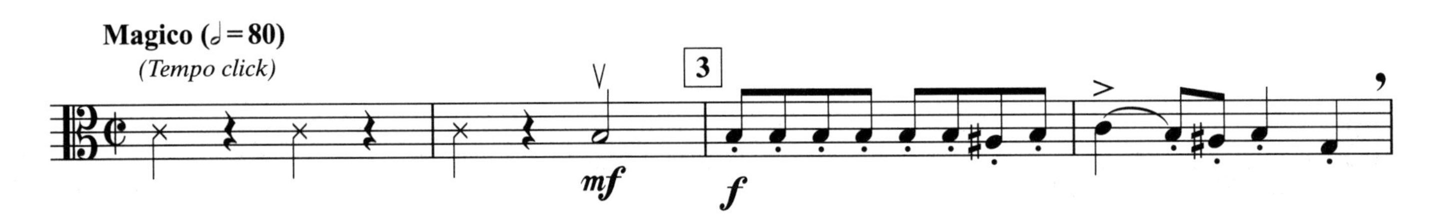

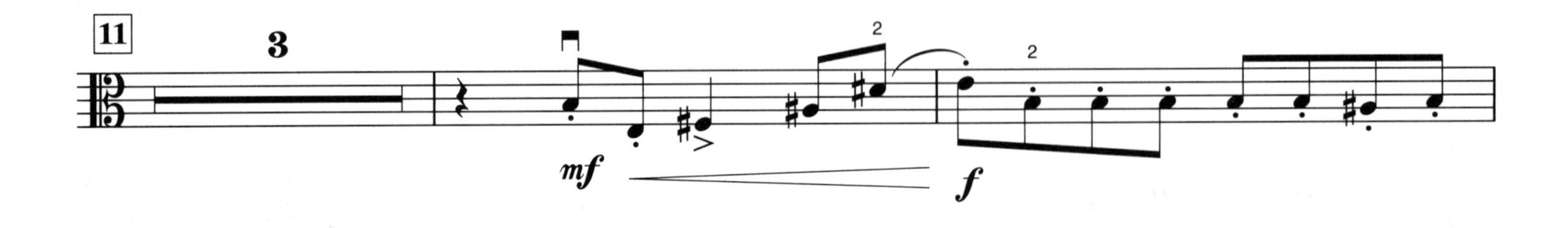

*An easier 8th-note alternative figure has been provided.

mf
3
f
31
3
f
43
mp
f

HOGWARTS' MARCH

By PATRICK DOYLE

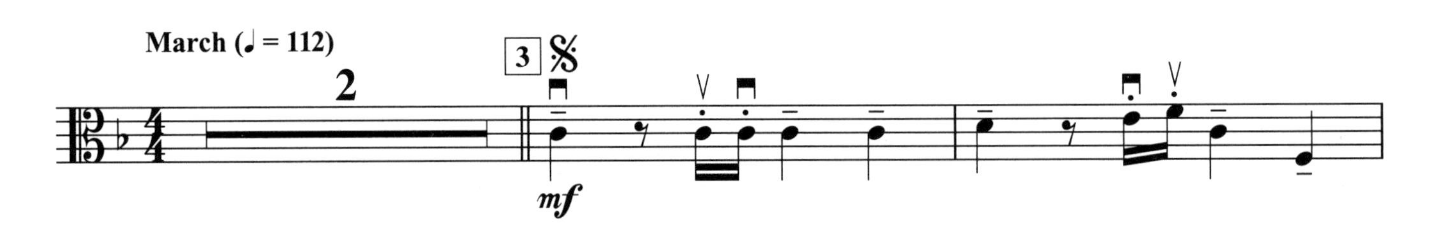

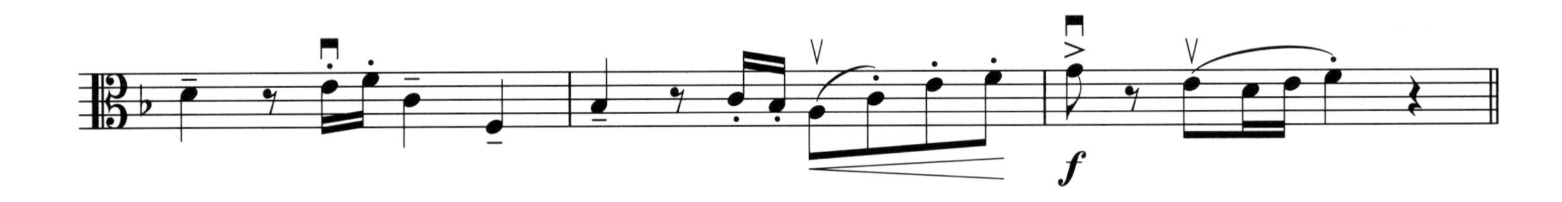

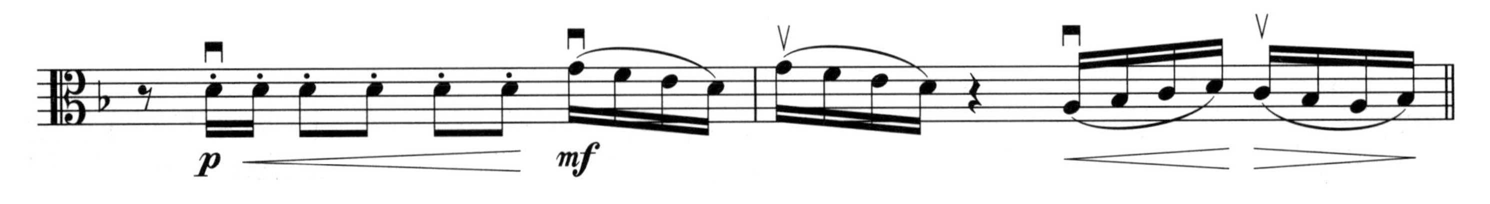

19
mf
To Coda
f
27
mp
mf
1.
2.
D.S. al Coda
Coda
f

HOGWARTS' HYMN

By PATRICK DOYLE

A WINDOW TO THE PAST

Music by
JOHN WILLIAMS

Harry Potter and The Sorcerer's Stone

Hedwig's Theme
Harry's Wondrous World

Harry Potter and The Chamber of Secrets

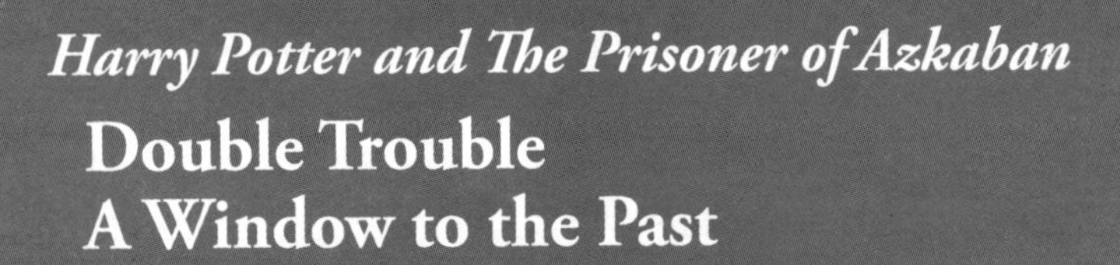

Nimbus 2000
Fawkes The Phoenix

Harry Potter and The Prisoner of Azkaban

Double Trouble
A Window to the Past

Harry Potter and The Goblet of Fire

Hogwarts' March
Hogwarts' Hymn

Harry Potter and The Order of the Phoenix

Professor Umbridge
Fireworks

Harry Potter Instrumental Solos • Viola

This book is part of an instrumental series arranged for Violin, Viola, and Cello. The arrangements are completely compatible with each other and can be played together or as solos. Each book features a specially designed piano accompaniment that can be easily played by a teacher or intermediate piano students, and a carefully crafted removable part, complete with bowings, articulations, and keys well suited for the Level 2–3 player. A fully orchestrated accompaniment CD is also provided. Each song on the CD includes a DEMO track, which features a live string performance, followed by a the PLAY-ALONG track by itself.

This book is also part of a Harry Potter Instrumental Solos (Movies 1–5) series written for Flute, Clarinet, Alto Sax, Tenor Sax, Trumpet, Horn in F, and Trombone. An orchestrated accompaniment CD is included. A piano accompaniment book (optional) is also available. Due to level considerations regarding keys and instrument ranges, the arrangements in the wind instrument series are not compatible with those in the string series.

Alfred

alfred.com

66
mf

82 Victoriously
f
90 Broadly
8vb

*The top cue notes are provided as a performing alternative.

117
f
rit.
a tempo
ff
8vb

PROFESSOR UMBRIDGE

By NICHOLAS HOOPER

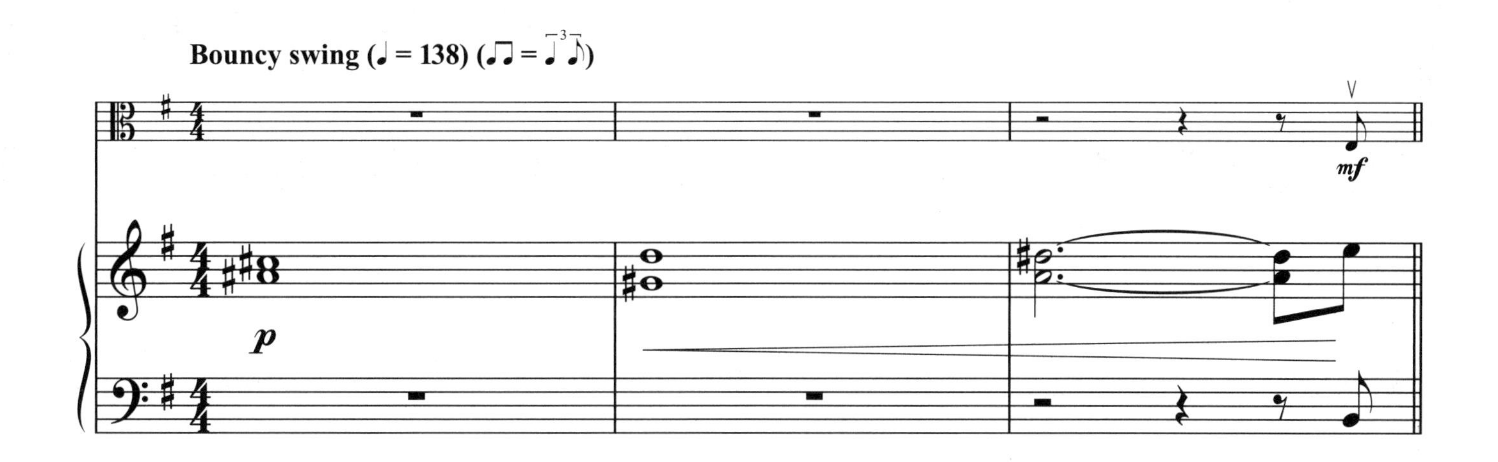

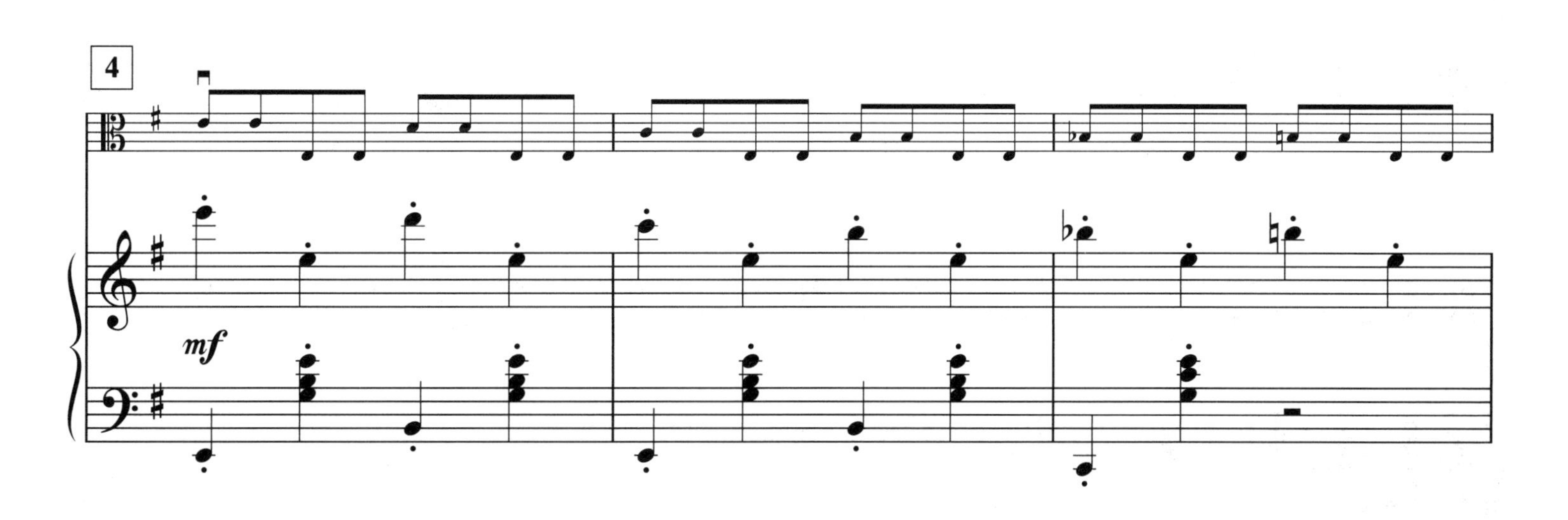

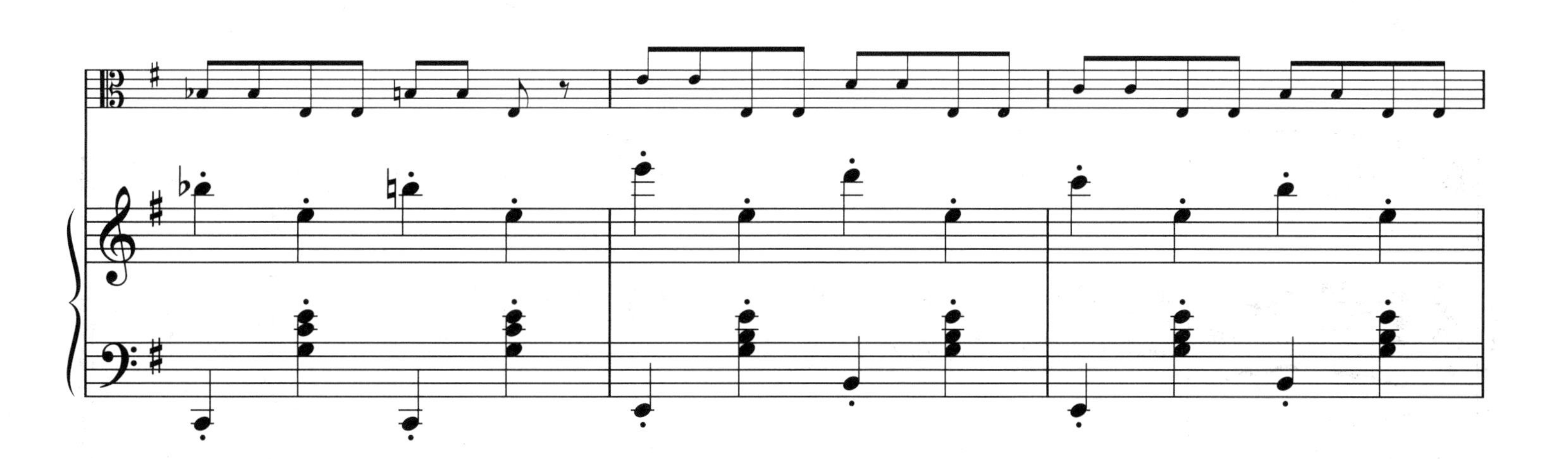

mp
mp
22
mf
mf

31
mp
mp
f
f
mp
mp

42
mf
mf
mf
mf
(V)

mp
p
57
f
p
8vb

NIMBUS 2000

Music by
JOHN WILLIAMS

*An easier 8th-note alternative figure has been provided.

31
decresc. poco a poco

43
mp
f
mp
f

HOGWARTS' MARCH

By PATRICK DOYLE

11
19

To Coda
f
f
27
mp
mp

mf
mf
1.
2.
D.S. 𝄋 al Coda
𝄌 Coda
f
f

HOGWARTS' HYMN

By PATRICK DOYLE

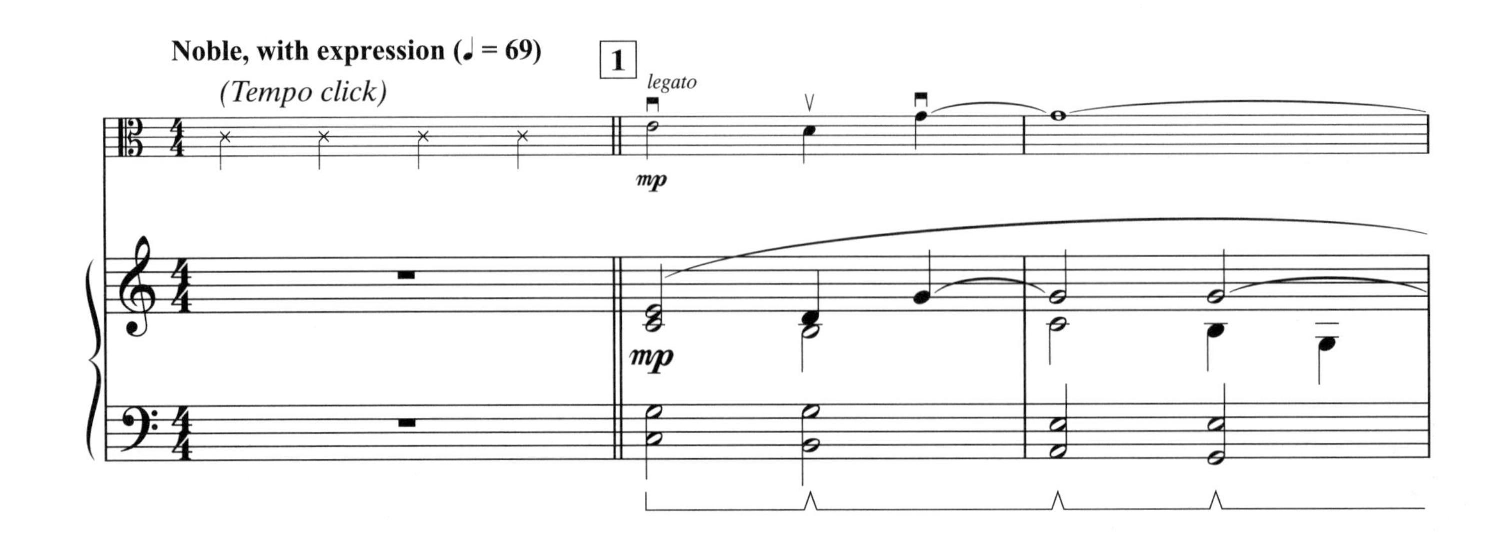

9
17

* The cue notes represent more challenging alternative notes.

36
a tempo
mf
poco rit.
f
mf
poco rit.
f
a tempo
molto rit.
molto rit.
8vb

A WINDOW TO THE PAST

Music by
JOHN WILLIAMS

Slowly and tenderly (♩. = 54)

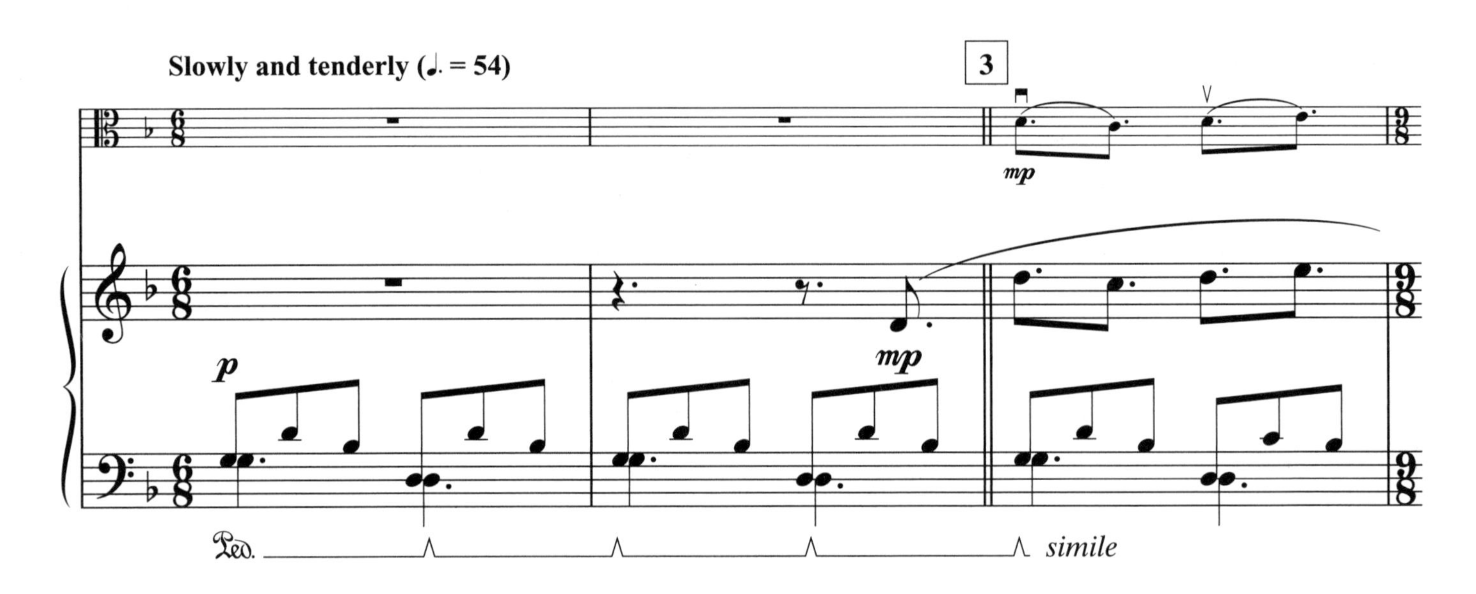

14
sim.
mf
mf

24
mf
r.h.
28
mf
mf cresc. poco a poco
accel. poco a poco
mp
cresc. poco a poco
mf
accel. poco a poco

37 Tempo I
mp
ff
mp
8vb
47
p
p
dim. e rit.
pp
dim. e rit.
pp

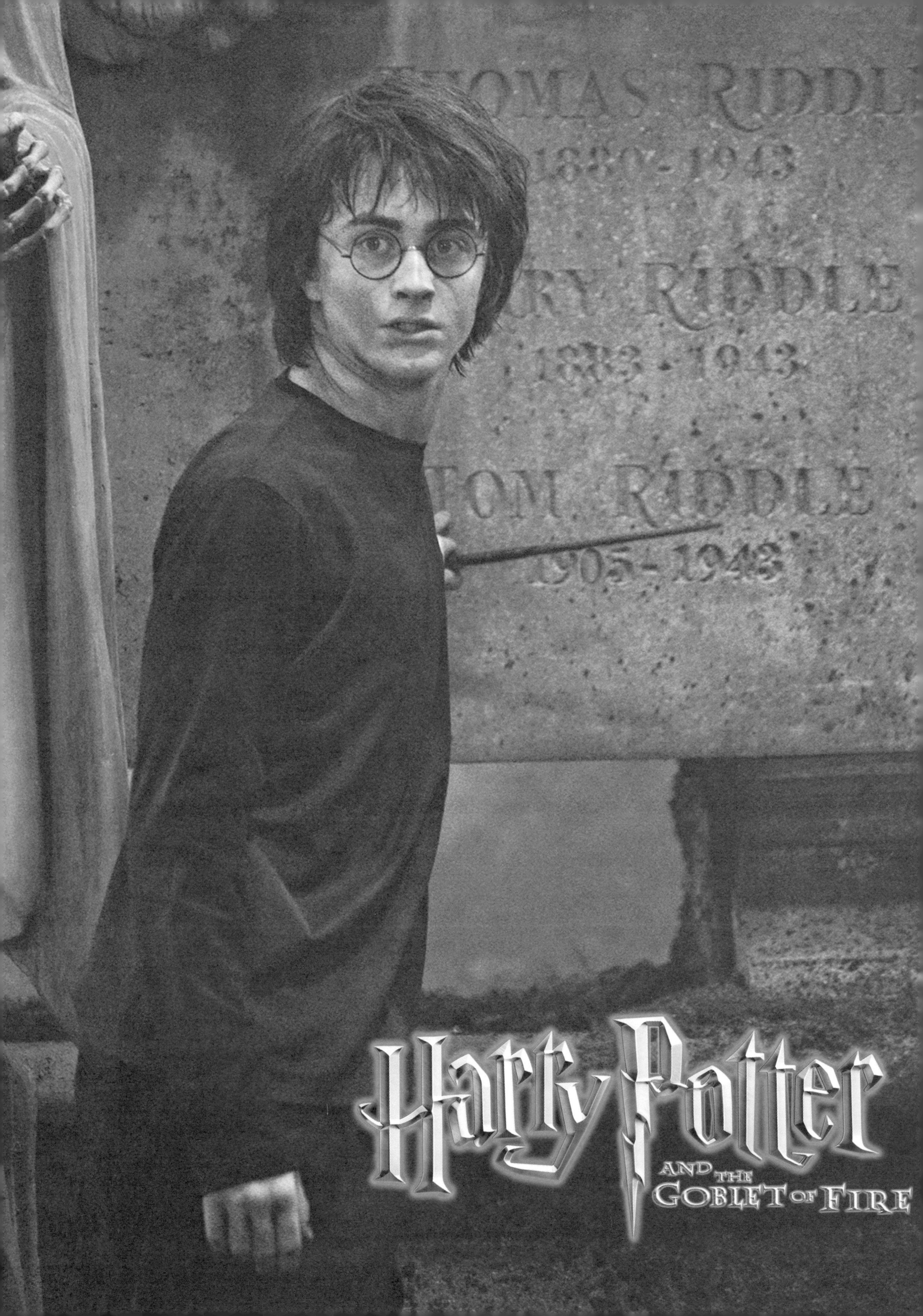

Harry Potter
AND THE
GOBLET OF FIRE

Harry Potter and the Prisoner of Azkaban

Harry Potter
AND THE
ORDER
OF THE
PHOENIX